The Treasure Map

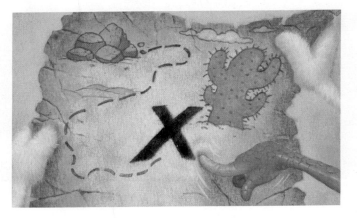

by Delilah Sampson
illustrated by Richard Bernal

 HOUGHTON MIFFLIN   BOSTON

Copyright © by Houghton Mifflin Company. All rights reserved.

Printed in China

ISBN-13: 978-0-547-02829-3
ISBN-10: 0-547-02829-6

13 14 15 16 0940 17 16 15 14
4500496268

The sun was hot.
Jack and his friends were playing
hopscotch. It was Jack's turn.
"One, two, three, four, five!"
Jack counted as he hopped.
He saw a paper in the sand.

"What is this?" said Jack.
He dug up the paper and
showed it to his friends.
"It looks very old," said Ned.
Liz looked at the paper.
"It's a map!" she cried.

3

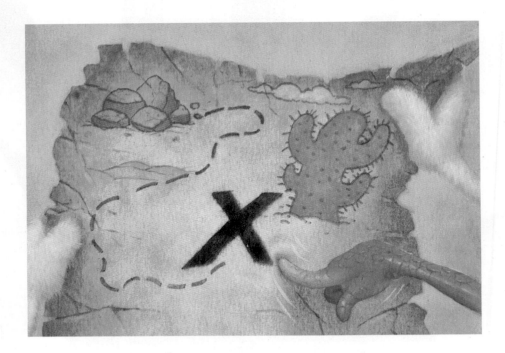

Liz pointed to a big black X
on the paper.
"I think it's a treasure map,"
she said. "An X always marks
the spot where the treasure is."
"Let's look for the treasure!"
said Jack. "Maybe it's gold coins!"

So the friends walked
through the desert.
They looked at the map
as they walked.
Jack held the map,
and Ned looked for clues.

Liz climbed up on the rocks.
She jumped from rock to rock
and looked for clues.
Liz was not as big as Jack
and Ned, but she wanted to
help, too!

At last, Jack stopped.

He pointed to the map.

"I think the treasure is here,"
Jack said.

Jack and Ned began to dig a
hole in the sand.

Then Ned yelled, "Here it is!"

Ned and Jack pulled a treasure
chest out of the hole.
Jack opened the chest.
The three friends looked inside
and saw a small cactus plant,
a rock, and a twig.
"This isn't treasure!" Liz said.

The three friends were sad.
Then Jack said, "Wait!
This twig is a treasure to me.
I'll eat it for dinner."
"And I can drink the water
inside this cactus," said Ned.
"The cactus is a treasure to me!"

"I get it!" said Liz.
"I get cold at night. This warm
rock will keep my body warm.
The rock is a treasure to me!"
That day, the three friends
learned that treasures are not
always made of gold!

Responding

The things the animals find in the box are treasures. What three details tell you why? Make a chart.

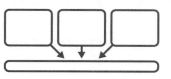

✎ Write About It

Text to Self Draw three pictures of things that are treasures to you. Write a sentence about your favorite.

five	**starts**
four	**three**
into	**two**
over	**watch**

✔ TARGET SKILL **Conclusions**

Use details to figure out more about the text.

✔ TARGET STRATEGY **Infer/Predict**

Use clues to figure out more about story parts.

GENRE A **fantasy** is a story that could not happen in real life.